A Four-tongued
ALPHABET

A Four-tongued
ALPHABET

Ruth Brown

An alphabet book in four languages

RED FOX

A Note on the Spanish Alphabet

The Spanish alphabet contains two additional letters which have not been illustrated in this book. The 13th letter is *ll* as in *llave* which means *key*, and the 16th letter is *ñ* as in *piña* which means *pineapple*.

A Red Fox Book

Published by Random Century Children's Books
20 Vauxhall Bridge Road, London SW1V 2SA

A division of the Random Century Group
London Melbourne Sydney Auckland
Johannesburg and agencies throughout the world

First published by Andersen Press Ltd 1991

Red Fox edition 1992

Copyright © Ruth Brown 1991

The right of Ruth Brown to be identified as the author of this
work has been asserted by her in accordance with the Copyright,
Designs and Patents Act, 1988.

Printed in Hong Kong

ISBN 0 09 997890 3

A a

ark · arche · Arche · arca

B b

ball · balle · Ball · balón

chameleon · caméléon · Chamäleon · camaleón

D   d

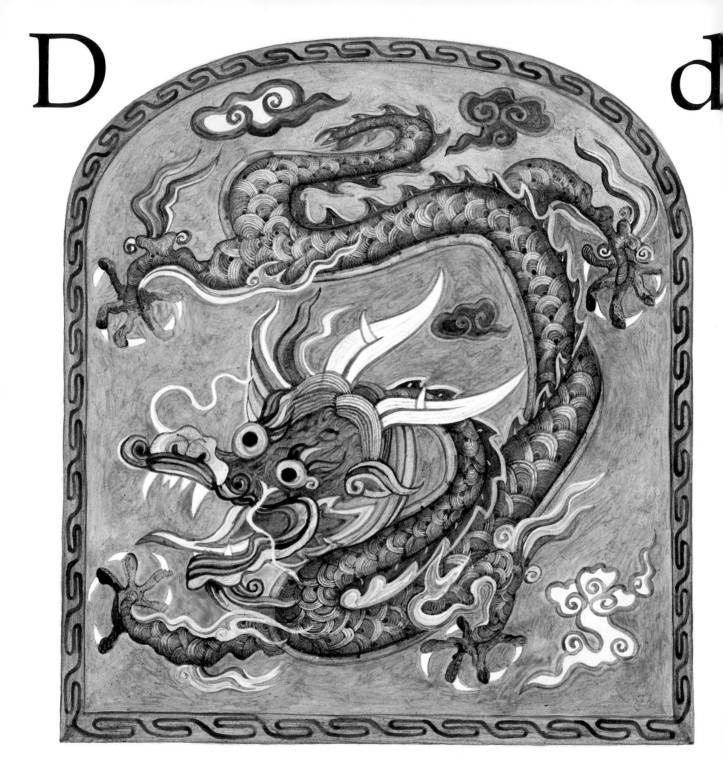

dragon · dragon · Drache · dragón

E e

elephant · éléphant · Elefant · elefante

F f

fire · feu · Feuer · fuego

G g

gorilla · gorille · Gorilla · gorila

H h

hamster · hamster · Hamster · hamster

I   i

insect · insecte · Insekt · insecto

J   j

jaguar · jaguar · Jaguar · jaguar

K k

kiwi · kiwi · Kiwi · kiwi

L l

labyrinth · labyrinthe · Labyrinth · laberinto

M m

magic · magie · Magie · magia

nose · nez · Nase · nariz

O

O

orchid · orchidée · Orchidee · orquidea

P
P

pyramid · pyramide · Pyramide · pirámide

quintet · quintette · Quintett · quinteto

R   r

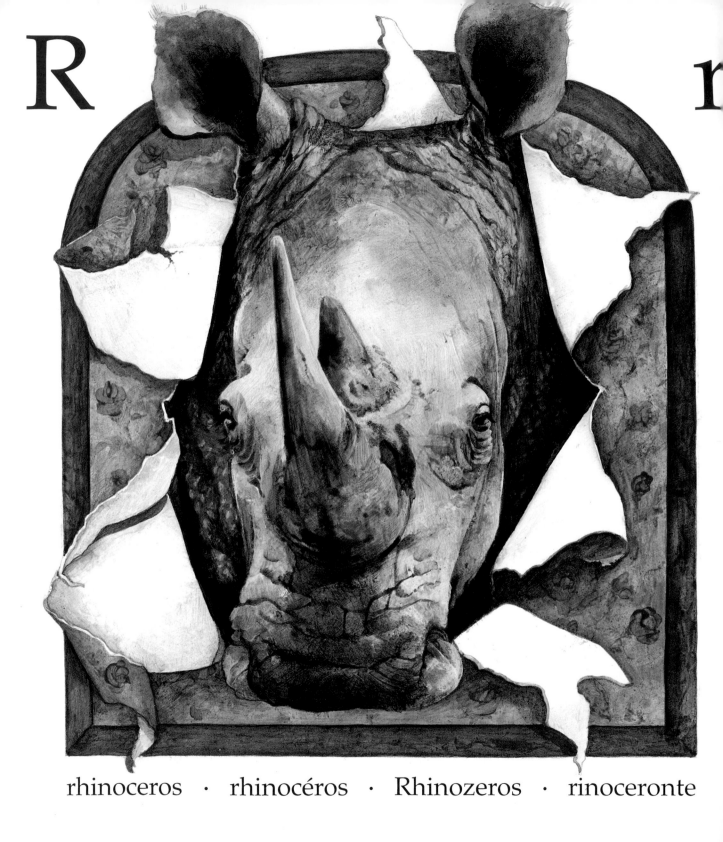

rhinoceros · rhinocéros · Rhinozeros · rinoceronte

S

S

snake · serpent · Schlange · serpiente

T t

tiger · tigre · Tiger · tigre

U   u

universe · univers · Universum · universo

V V

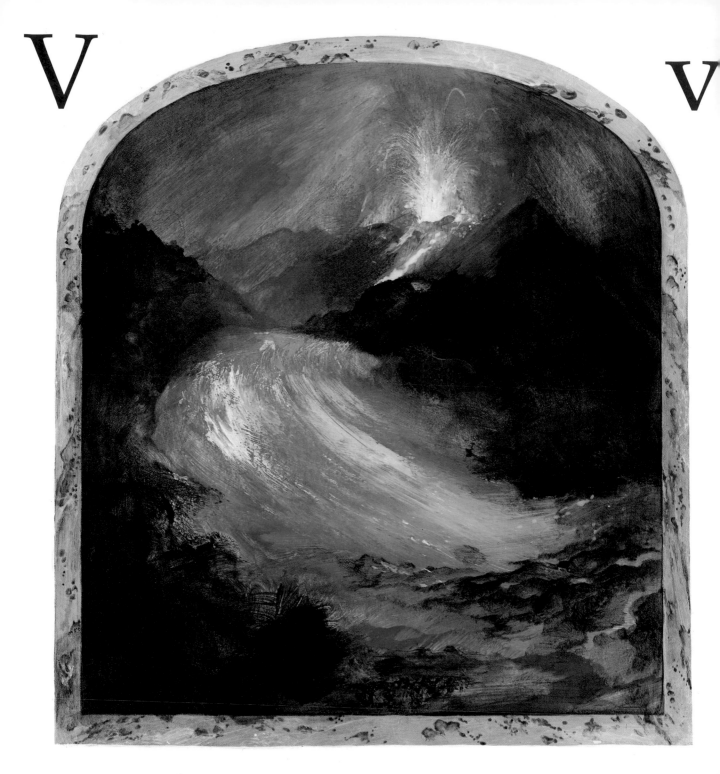

volcano · volcan · Vulkan · volcán

W W

water-polo · water-polo · Wasserball · water-polo

X   X

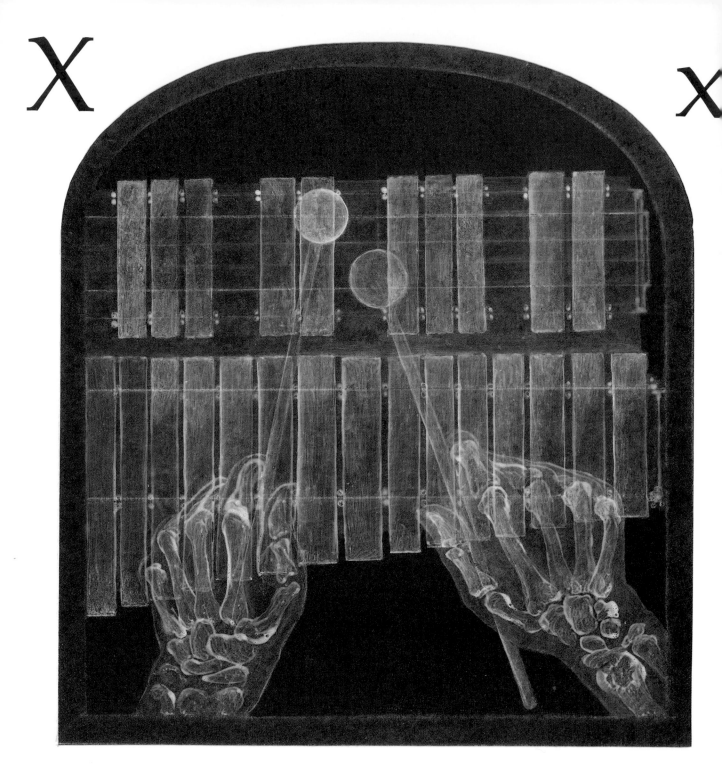

xylophone · xylophone · Xylophon · xilófono

Y y

yeti · yeti · Yeti · yeti

Z z

zig-zag · zig-zag · Zickzack · zig-zag

		English	**French**	**German**	**Spanish**
A	a	ark	arche	Arche	arca
B	b	ball	balle	Ball	balón
C	c	chameleon	caméléon	Chamäleon	camaleón
D	d	dragon	dragon	Drache	dragón
E	e	elephant	éléphant	Elefant	elefante
F	f	fire	feu	Feuer	fuego
G	g	gorilla	gorille	Gorilla	gorila
H	h	hamster	hamster	Hamster	hamster
I	i	insect	insecte	Insekt	insecto
J	j	jaguar	jaguar	Jaguar	jaguar
K	k	kiwi	kiwi	Kiwi	kiwi
L	l	labyrinth	labyrinthe	Labyrinth	laberinto
M	m	magic	magie	Magie	magia
N	n	nose	nez	Nase	nariz
O	o	orchid	orchidée	Orchidee	orquidea
P	p	pyramid	pyramide	Pyramide	pirámide
Q	q	quintet	quintette	Quintett	quinteto
R	r	rhinoceros	rhinocéros	Rhinozeros	rinoceronte
S	s	snake	serpent	Schlange	serpiente
T	t	tiger	tigre	Tiger	tigre
U	u	universe	univers	Universum	universo
V	v	volcano	volcan	Vulkan	volcán
W	w	water-polo	water-polo	Wasserball	water-polo
X	x	xylophone	xylophone	Xylophon	xilófono
Y	y	yeti	yeti	Yeti	yeti
Z	z	zig-zag	zig-zag	Zickzack	zig-zag

Some bestselling Red Fox picture books

THE BIG ALFIE AND ANNIE ROSE STORYBOOK
by Shirley Hughes
OLD BEAR
by Jane Hissey
JOHN PATRICK NORMAN MCHENNESSY –
THE BOY WHO WAS ALWAYS LATE
by John Burningham
I WANT A CAT
by Tony Ross
NOT NOW, BERNARD
by David McKee
THE STORY OF HORRIBLE HILDA AND HENRY
by Emma Chichester Clark
THE SAND HORSE
by Michael Foreman and Ann Turnbull
BAD BORIS GOES TO SCHOOL
by Susie Jenkin-Pearce
MRS PEPPERPOT AND THE BILBERRIES
by Alf Prøysen
BAD MOOD BEAR
by John Richardson
WHEN SHEEP CANNOT SLEEP
by Satoshi Kitamura
THE LAST DODO
by Ann and Reg Cartwright
IF AT FIRST YOU DO NOT SEE
by Ruth Brown
THE MONSTER BED
by Jeanne Willis and Susan Varley
DR XARGLE'S BOOK OF EARTHLETS
by Jeanne Willis and Tony Ross
JAKE
by Deborah King